Jane Smisor Bastien • Lisa Bastien •

BASTIENS'
COLLAGE
OF SOLOS

Bastiens' Collage of Solos, Book 4, is designed to captivate the interest and imagination of early intermediate students with the three distinctive styles of Jane, Lisa, and Lori Bastien. These solos will add excitement to the repertoire for intermediate students of all ages!

Contents

✔ *

*To reinforce the feeling of achievement, the teacher or student may put a ✔ when the page has been mastered.

ISBN 0-8497-9636-9

Best of Times

Lori Bastien

Whistle Stop Boogie

Jane Smisor Bastien

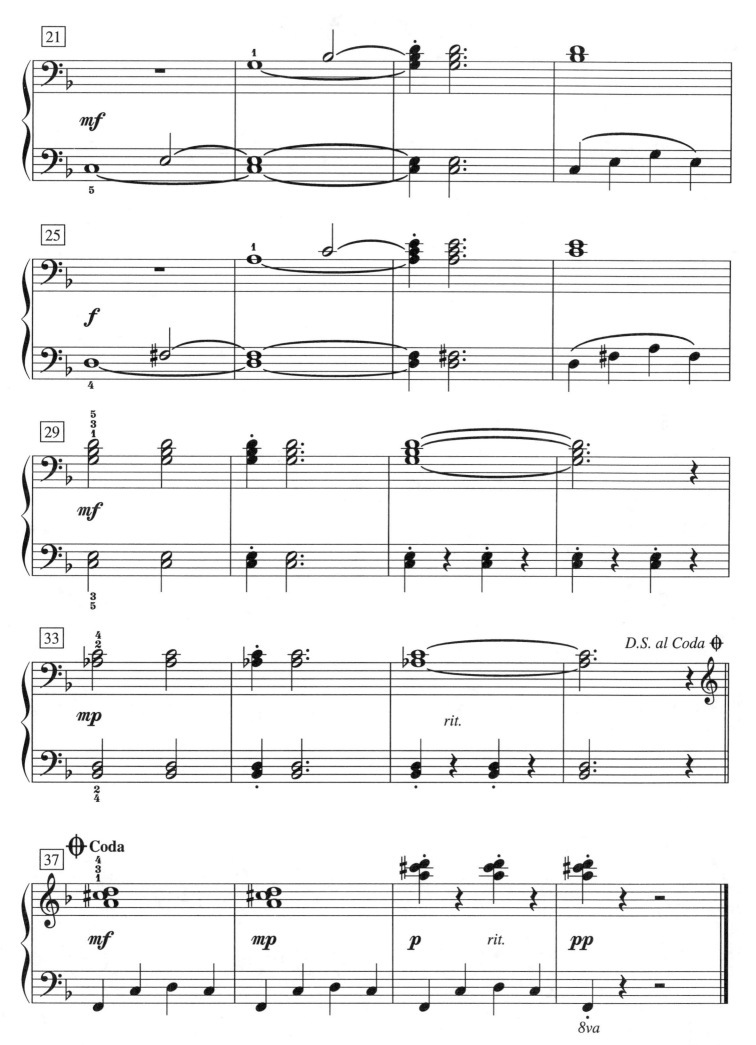

Swan Waltz

For Lauren Hanss

Lisa Bastien

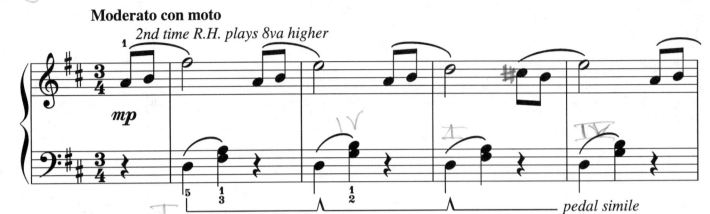

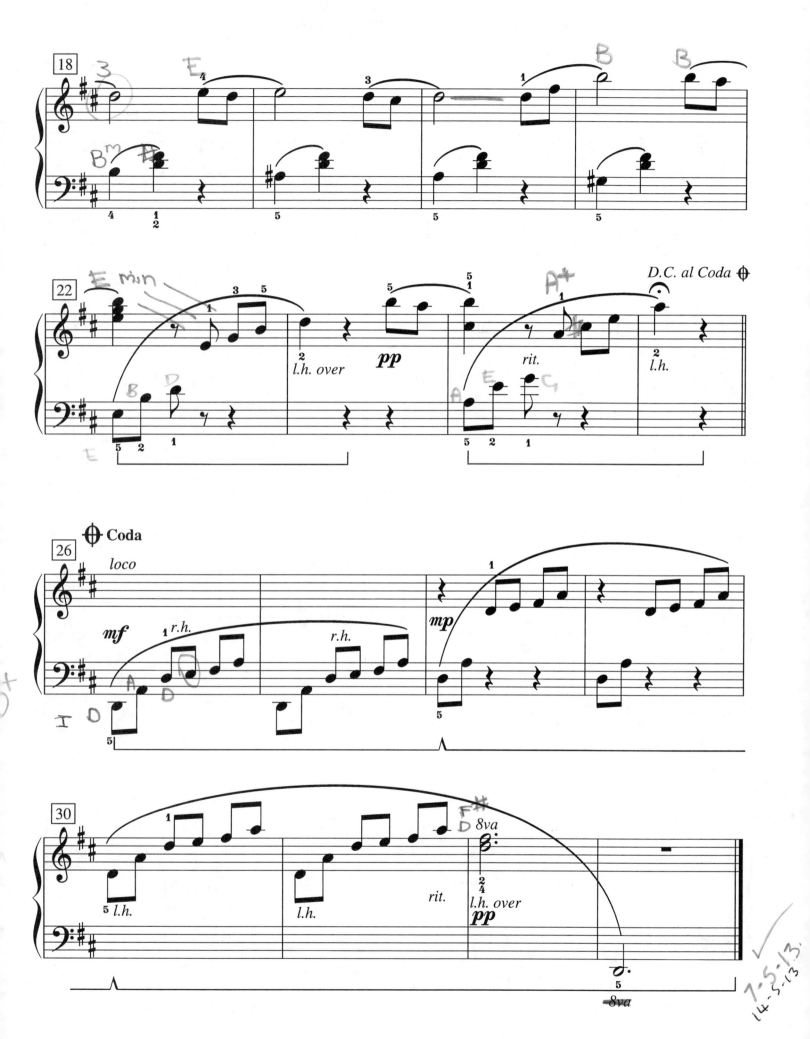

Flight of the Snowy Owl

Lisa Bastien

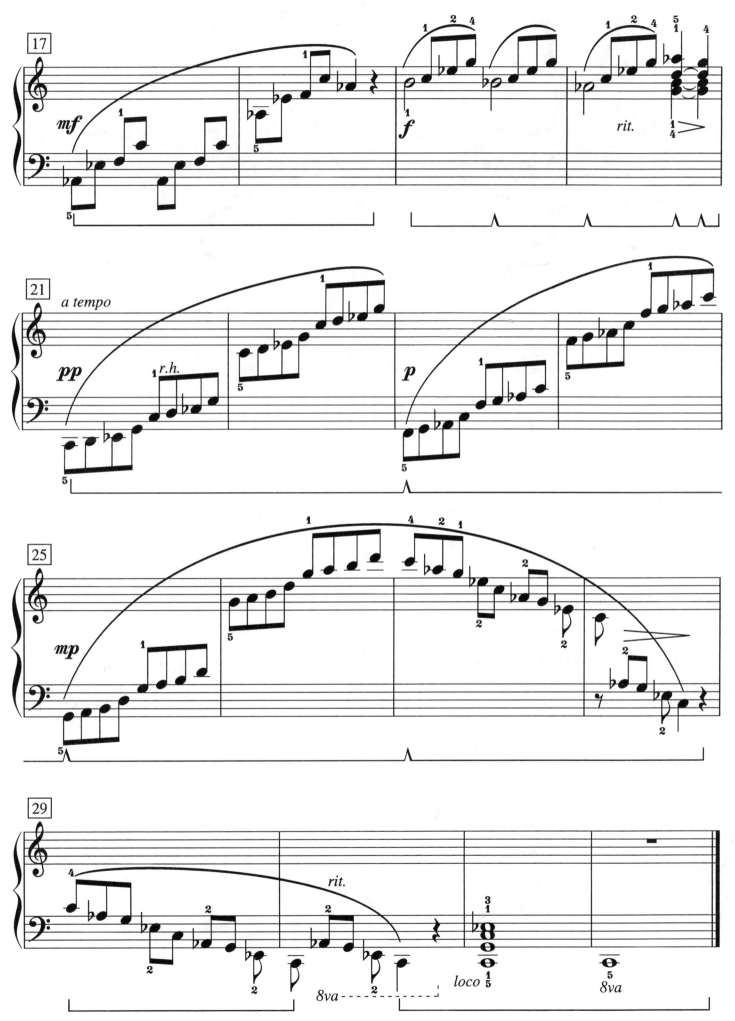

Holiday Down South

Lori Bastien

Canterbury Cathedral

Jane Smisor Bastien

Jazzin' in Manhattan

Lisa Bastien

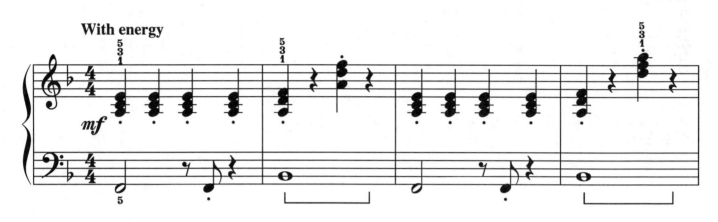

Whistling Pine Trees

Andante con moto

Lori Bastien

Galaxies Unknown

Jane Smisor Bastien

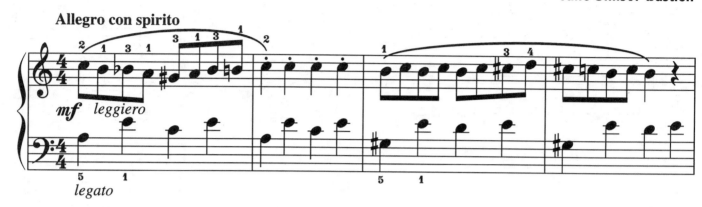

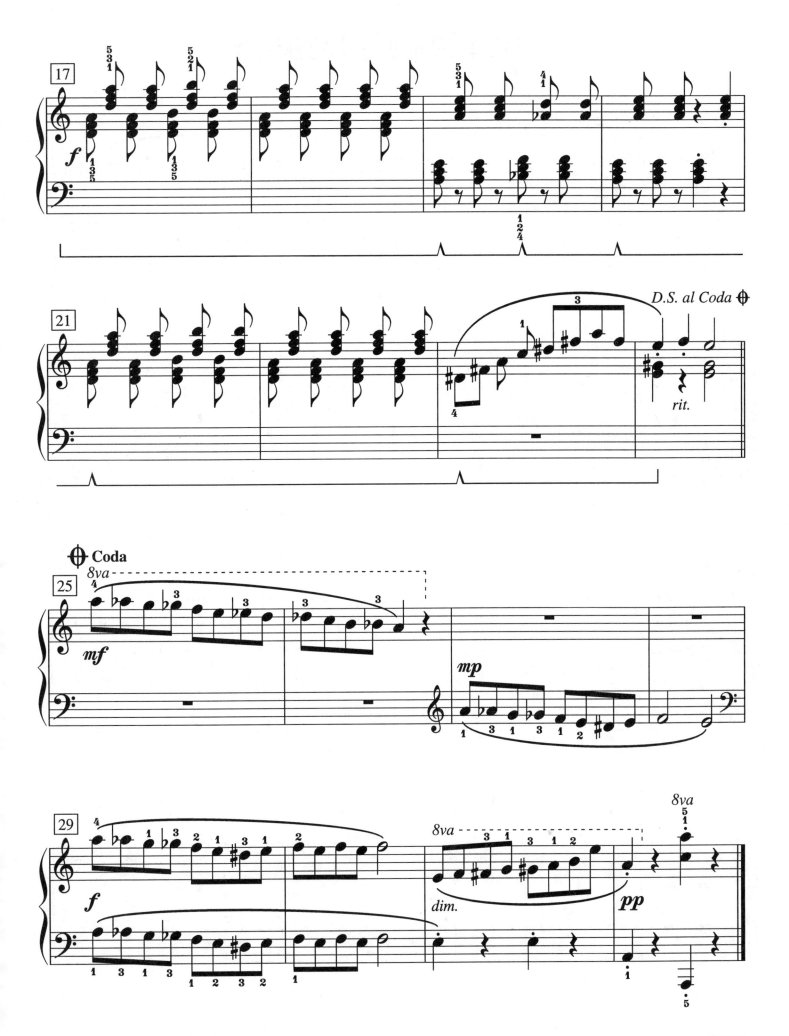

Musical Triathlon

Jane Smisor Bastien

Winter Rides

Lori Bastien

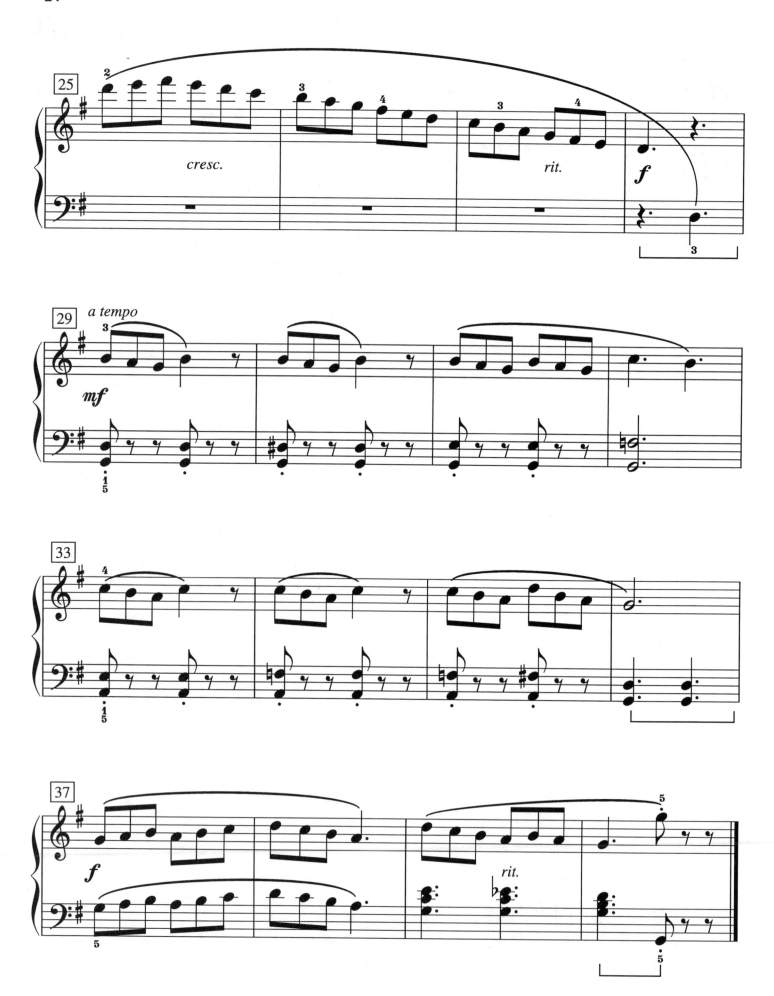